LITIGATING SPINAL CORD INJURIES

1998 Cumulative Supplement

This supplement supersedes the 1997 Supplement

LITIGATING SPINAL CORD INJURIES
LAW, MEDICINE AND ECONOMICS

1998 Cumulative Supplement

MARK R. KOSIERADZKI

Formerly published by
John Wiley & Sons, Inc.

ASPEN LAW & BUSINESS
A Division of Aspen Publishers, Inc.

Permissions
Aspen Law & Business
1185 Avenue of the Americas
New York, NY 10036

Printed in the United States of America

ISBN 0-7355-0072-X

About Aspen Law & Business

Aspen Law & Business—comprising the former Prentice Hall Law & Business, Little, Brown and Company's Professional Division, and Wiley Law Publications—is a leading publisher of authoritative treatises, practice manuals, services, and journals for attorneys, financial and tax advisors, corporate and bank directors, and other business professionals. Our mission is to provide practical solution-based how-to information keyed to the lates legislative, judicial, and regulatory developments.

We offer publications in the areas of banking and finance; bankruptcy; business and commercial law; corporate law; pensions, benefits, and labor; insurance law; securities; taxation; intellectual property; government and administrative law; matrimonial and family law; environmental and health law; international law; legal practice and litigation; and criminal law.

Other Aspen products treating personal injury issues include:

Anatomy and Physiology for Lawyers
Evaluating Temporomandibular Injuries
Handling General Surgery Cases
Head Trauma Cases: Law and Medicine (Second Edition)
Litigating TMJ Cases
Orthopedic Disability and Expert Testimony

ASPEN LAW & BUSINESS
A Division of Aspen Publishers, Inc.
A Wolters Kluwer Company

SUBSCRIPTION NOTICE

This Aspen Law & Business product is updated on a periodic basis with supplements to reflect important changes in the subject matter. If you purchased this product directly from Aspen Law & Business, we have already recorded your subscription for the update service.

If, however, you purchased this product from a bookstore and wish to receive future updates and revised or related volumes billed separately with a 30-day examination review, please contact our Customer Service Department at 1-800-234-1660 or send your name, company name (if applicable), address, and title of the product to:

Aspen Law & Business
A Division of Aspen Publishers, Inc.
7201 McKinney Circle
Frederick, MD 21701

CONTENTS

Note to the Reader: *Materials that appear only in the supplement and not in the main volume are listed below in boldface type.*

Chapter 4 Overview of Spinal Cord Injury Epidemiology and Long-term Outcomes

Chapter 9 Life Care Plan

§ 9.11A Home Modification

Chapter 15 Defense's Annuity Expert

§ 15.7A Cross Examination of the Defense's Annuity Expert

Chapter 16 The Use of Nonexpert Damages Witnesses

§ 16.3 An SCI Victim's Perspective

Chapter 17 Biomechanics of Injury

§ 17.1 Anatomy of Spine

§ 17.2 Application of Engineering Principles

§ 17.3 Mechanism of Spinal Cord Injury

§ 17.4 Use of a Biomechanical Expert

§ 17.5 Qualifying the Biomechanical Engineer

§ 17.6 Variety of Uses for the Biomechanical Expert's Expertise

§ 17.7 Conclusion

Table of Cases

Index

PREFACE

In an effort to respond to the requests of the readers of *Litigating Spinal Cord Injuries,* we have added a section to Chapter 9, Life Care Plan, expanded Chapter 15, Defense's Annuity Expert, to include actual examples of the cross-examination, and added a new section to Chapter 16. In addition Chapter 17, Biomechanics of Injury, was added to enhance the ability of advocates to understand the injury by understanding the forces and mechanisms necessary to inflict the harm. As our understanding grows, so does our ability to help those who have entrusted their cases to us.

MARK R. KOSIERADZKI

CHAPTER 4

OVERVIEW OF SPINAL CORD INJURY EPIDEMIOLOGY AND LONG-TERM OUTCOMES

Michael J. DeVivo

§ 4.9 Long-term Survival

***Page 64.** Replace Table 4-1 with:*

Current Age	Life Expectancy (Years)					
	Not Ventilator Dependent					Ventilator Dependent
	No SCI	Motor Functional Any Level	Paraplegia	Tetraplegia C5-C8	Tetraplegia C1-C4	Any Level
20 years	56.9	51.7	45.4	40.5	37.1	26.9
40 years	38.3	33.6	28.0	24.0	21.3	13.9
60 years	21.1	17.3	13.1	10.3	8.4	4.1

Life expectancy for SCI persons surviving at least 1 year post-injury.
[Values for persons with no SCI are from the 1992 U.S. Life Tables for the general population.]

CHAPTER 9

LIFE CARE PLAN

John E. Dahlberg

Page 146. *Add the following new section after § 9.11:*

§ 9.11A Home Modification

Shannon McGurran

Most individuals who become disabled as a result of a spinal cord injury (SCI) must use a wheelchair for mobility. As a result, many such individuals find they are unable to enter and maneuver within their existing home. Architectural modifications are necessary to allow the individual to maneuver freely, independently, and safely in and around the home. When a home is not wheelchair accessible, the individual with the disability must rely on others for most of his daily care and, until appropriate modifications are made, may have to use an inappropriately converted living room or dining room as a bedroom and make-shift bathroom.

An appropriate housing report is an analysis of accessible housing options. The report generally identifies existing barriers within the existing home and reviews potential solutions for improving accessibility. The solutions may be a combination of architectural modifications and selection of products that promote greater accessibility.

Federal standards and state building codes governing accessibility exist, but they are designed for application in public and commercial settings and do not apply to single-family homes. One reason for exempting single-family homes is that individuals with disabilities have different abilities and, to maximize their independence, their homes should be designed to accommodate their unique needs.

Thus, home modifications chosen should reflect:

- the type of mobility aid;
- the size of the mobility aid;

- the space required to use the mobility aid;
- the individual's high and low reach ranges;
- the individual's hand dexterity;
- the type of transfers required;
- the individual's involvement in completing daily chores;
- anticipated changes in the individual's abilities; and
- the age of the individual.

In general, it is useful for the person completing the appropriate housing report to ask the injured person's physical therapist, physician, or life care planner for assistance in determining the extent of the modifications that may be necessary.

If the injured person has personal care attendants, modifications should be designed to increase the safety of the caregivers as well as that of the person they are caring for. It is important to provide features that will help the caregivers avoid fatigue or injury that might prevent them from caring for the injured person. For example, providing lifting equipment to assist in transfers will help the caregivers avoid potential back injuries.

It is also important to provide the injured person with tools to maximize his independence in caring for himself. Even if the level of disability requires full-time personal care attendants, it is important not to assume that the personal care attendants will do everything for the client, thereby eliminating the need for modifications. For example, if the person with the disability is able to turn on the faucet hardware at the bathroom sink but is unable to brush his teeth, accessible faucet hardware should be provided so that the individual can participate in and take some responsibility for his personal care and interact with his environment. The performance of even simple tasks can give the individual with the disability a sense of accomplishment.

Typical Modifications to A Standard Home

The following modifications are examples of typical changes that need to be made to a standard home to accommodate a person using a wheelchair:

- The width of the existing garage may need to be widened to accommodate a van for transporting the person using a wheelchair or transfers to a vehicle. Adequate maneuvering space must be provided around the vehicle and at the entrance to the home. The garage may also need to accommodate a ramp or lifting device. An attached garage is preferred as it allows the individual in the wheelchair to maneuver from house to parked vehicle without being exposed to rain, snow, and cold temperatures.

- Overhead garage doors generally need to be replaced with taller garage doors that will allow a van with a raised roof to pass through.
- Ramps must be constructed alongside or in place of existing steps at entrance doors.
- Thresholds at doorways and abrupt transitions between floor surfaces should be removed or beveled.
- Lifting equipment must be installed to provide access to different levels within the home. There is a variety of equipment styles. A stair lift is a chair that rides over the stairway and requires the individual to be able to transfer from the wheelchair onto the stair lift. For individuals who can not transfer safely, options include incline platform lifts (the wheelchair rolls onto a platform that rides over stairs), vertical platform lifts (which operate in the same way as elevators), or elevators. Other factors that may impact the choice of lifting equipment include the configuration of the existing stairway and the distance to be covered.
- Typical doors are too narrow for a wheelchair to pass through and must be widened.
- Hallways are typically too narrow to accommodate a wheelchair turning into doorways and must be widened.
- Typical bathrooms do not provide adequate maneuvering space to accommodate a wheelchair and must be widened. Providing a clear floor space at least 60" in diameter between fixtures will allow the wheelchair to turn a full circle, giving the individual access to the toilet, sink, shower, and/or bathtub.
- Bathroom vanities must be modified or replaced to provide clear knee space below the sink so the wheelchair can roll up to the sink. Drawers should be installed adjacent to the knee space to provide easy-to-reach storage for personal care items.
- Mirrors need to be lowered or replaced so the person seated in a wheelchair can look into them.
- Some persons with SCI are able to transfer onto a toilet. For a safe transfer, it is important that the height of the toilet seat be level with

the seat of the wheelchair. Since the typical residential toilet has a seat much lower than the seat of a wheelchair, it should be replaced with a "handicap" model that offers a seat height 17" to 22" from the floor. Grab bars are needed next to the toilet to assist in completing safe transfers.

- It is important to provide clear floor space in front of or alongside the toilet so the wheelchair can approach the toilet. The individual's abilities will determine the most appropriate position for the wheelchair to be placed next to the toilet for transferring. Clear floor space at the toilet is also important for persons who need to empty leg bags.
- Most persons with SCI find it easiest to bathe in a roll-in shower. The size of the shower and the type of equipment required depend on the individual's ability to transfer. Shower sizes vary from 36" x 36" for persons who use fold-down bench seats to 60" x 60" for persons who use shower chairs. The shower should not have a curb. It should incorporate accessories such as a hand-held shower head, grab bars, fold-down bench seat (if the individual has good trunk control and is able to transfer and sit unsupported), and controls that are easily reachable. A person who can not use a fold-down bench seat should use a shower chair, a chair on wheels that can be rolled into the shower.
- Installation of a whirlpool bath is recommended, as it helps to relax rigid muscles and maintain skin condition. Lifting equipment is usually needed for transferring the individual into and out of the bathtub, and some individuals may require a bath chair for additional support.
- Storage is needed for commode chairs, shower chairs, and bath chairs.
- Changing benches in the bathroom or bedroom may be appropriate to accommodate individuals who wear diapers.
- Typical bedrooms are too small to provide maneuvering space for the wheelchair. Plan on providing a clear floor space at least 60" in diameter to one side of the bed, in front of the closet, and adjacent to the dresser.
- Because dresser drawers can be difficult to open from a wheelchair, it is recommended that large closets be provided. Closets should have adjustable closet rods and shelves that can be mounted low enough to be reached by an individual seated in a wheelchair.
- Providing the individual who has a disability with a ground floor bedroom facilitates his evacuation in the event of an emergency. For

safety, it is recommended that an emergency exit door and ramp be provided from the bedroom.

- Maneuvering a manually operated wheelchair over a carpet is difficult—especially for persons with limited strength. Carpets (unless low pile and densely woven) should be replaced with a firm flooring material such as hardwood, laminate flooring, or ceramic tile. The material chosen should be of a quality that will accommodate the weight of a wheelchair and the abuse resulting from making tight turns with the wheelchair.
- Controls such as thermostats, light switches, and electrical outlets—which are typically mounted outside accessible reach ranges for persons seated in a wheelchair—must be lowered.
- Additional electrical power may be necessary to accommodate equipment such as an electric wheelchair, ventilators, and so forth.
- A laundry room located in close proximity to the accessible bedroom is helpful, as there is typically an increase in the amount of soiled laundry. For individuals who are able to wash their own clothes, front-loading washers and dryers are more accessible than the top-loading models.
- Air-conditioning may need to be installed to assist in maintenance of the injured individual's body temperature. Many physicians will prescribe air-conditioning for their SCI patients.
- If the life care plan calls for a live-in personal care attendant, the housing options report should address the provision of a bedroom, bathroom, and living area for the attendant. A full-scale apartment need not be provided, but reserving a separate area in the home for the personal care attendant is recommended, as it affords privacy to both the attendant and the family. If an outside personal care attendant is required to stay overnight, it is recommended that a sitting room be provided in close proximity to the accessible bedroom. This allows the attendant to be close enough to monitor the patient, but not stay in the room where the patient is sleeping. Some families prefer to have a separate entrance for personal care attendants, which enables the attendants to enter and exit the home with minimal interruption to the injured person's family.

The extent of recommended modifications to be made to a kitchen depends on the involvement the person with the disability will have in meal preparation. This involvement may depend on physical ability and/or personal desire. Where the individual with the disability wants to be able to cook independently, recommended modifications include:

- Providing a clear floor space at least 60" in diameter between cabinets and appliances so the wheelchair can move freely within the kitchen.
- Providing clear knee space below the sink so the person seated in the wheelchair can roll up to the sink.
- Installing single-lever faucet hardware at the sink if the person has a limited reach range and/or limited dexterity.
- Relocating the garbage disposal switch to a place that is easy to reach.
- Providing clear knee space below a work counter so the person seated in the wheelchair can roll up to the counter.
- Installing a cooktop with front-mounted easy-to-operate controls and clear knee space below.
- Installing a wall oven at a height where shelves inside the oven are within reach of the person seated in a wheelchair. An oven with a side-swinging door is preferable to one with a bottom-hinged door, as it does not require the user to reach over a hot oven door.
- Installing oven controls that are easy to operate for a person with limited dexterity.
- Providing a bread board, adjacent to the oven, to give the individual a space to place a hot pan after removing it from the oven.
- Providing base cabinets with pull-out shelves.
- Providing easy-to-operate cabinet and drawer hardware.
- Providing a pantry that offers generous storage space at heights that are easily reachable by the person seated in a wheelchair.
- Installing electrical outlets and fan switches within accessible reach ranges.

If the person with a disability does not desire to be the primary cook or does not have the ability to use an oven and/or cooktop, modifications to accommodate assistance in meal preparation or simple modifications to allow access to a microwave oven, a breadboard/work surface, a sink, and a portion of the cabinets are recommended.

In addition to the above-listed modifications, the following modifications should be considered for persons with limited dexterity:

- Replacing door knobs with lever hardware.
- Replacing doors that require use of a key to unlock with doors that are equipped with automatic opening devices. The individual with the disability carries a transmitter that sends a signal to unlock, open, close, and relock the door.
- Replacing faucet hardware at bathroom and kitchen sinks with single-lever or automatic sensor hardware.
- Replacing round knobs on closet doors and cabinets with D-shaped cabinet pulls.

Review Options to Modify Existing Homes

Rambler-style homes can usually be modified easily to become wheelchair accessible. In some instances, depending on the number of available bedrooms and the number of individuals living in the home, it is possible to remodel within the existing walls—for example, if there is a spare bedroom that can be split in half to provide additional floor space to an adjacent bathroom and accessible bedroom. In a home where there is no spare bedroom, the construction of a bedroom/bathroom addition is typically necessary. In a standard home, the bedroom and the bathroom are two critical locations where more generous floor space is needed.

Two-story homes that offer main-level bedrooms or that can accommodate a bedroom/bathroom addition can also be remodeled fairly easily as long as there are no sunken levels. Split-level homes are the most difficult to modify to accommodate a bedroom/bathroom expansion due to stairs and limited interior space. The installation of lifting equipment (such as a stair lift, platform lift, or elevator) is needed to provide access to all levels, but using lifting equipment several times a day to maneuver to different living areas within the home is more difficult for the individual in a wheelchair than it is to maneuver in a rambler-style home that could provide all living areas on the same level. Furthermore, the individual must rely on the continued operation of the equipment.

If modifications to make the existing home accessible are too difficult or extensive to be practical, it may be more appropriate to review the option of selling the existing home and purchasing another home that would better lend itself to remodeling. After identifying an area where the individual with a disability would like to live, a real estate agent can be retained to help identify suitable homes available for purchase.

Without the individual's entering into a purchase agreement, however, recommendations for modifying a potential home may need to be based on examples of appropriate modifications previously made to a similar-style home.

Rental Apartments

For most individuals disabled with SCI, a rental apartment is neither a preferred nor an appropriate choice. An apartment may be adequate for an individual who is single and plans on remaining single—especially if the individual was renting prior to the injury, but it is not a good long-term solution if the person with a disability is a child living with his parents or an adult living with children, a spouse, or a roommate.

There are very few truly accessible apartments that will accommodate individuals with SCI, especially those who require availability of a roll-in shower for bathing. Although federal laws currently mandate that new construction include the provision of accessible and easily adaptable units, in many communities a large portion of the rental units are in buildings that were constructed prior to the adoption of current federal standards and were not required to incorporate accessible housing units.

Rental units incorporating features of accessibility generally do not incorporate specific accessibility features needed by the person whose disability is the result of SCI. Typically, these units provide "generic" accessibility features that are designed to accommodate the "average" person with a disability. Rental units that provide greater levels of accessibility (such as a roll-in shower) are few and far between and generally provide 1- to 3-year waiting lists for new tenants.

Typical accessible rental units provide only one or two bedrooms, which is not adequate to accommodate a family with a disabled individual or an individual with a disability who is planning to have a family. Furthermore, typical accessible rental units do not provide appropriate age and/or family-style housing for many persons with disabilities because "accessible" units are typically located in senior housing or housing reserved solely for persons with disabilities.

Although an individual with a disability cannot be denied the opportunity to make a rental apartment accessible at his or her own expense, the owner of the building can require the individual to escrow funds to be used to return the apartment to its original condition upon termination of the rental agreement.

Finally, for individuals who were homeowners prior to their injury, a rental apartment—even an accessible rental apartment—does not provide a life style comparable to the life style they had enjoyed as homeowners.

Construction of a New Home

Modifications made to an existing home do not always blend into the surroundings and are not always satisfactory. For most individuals, construction of a new home is the option that provides the greatest level of accessibility, dispensing with "band aid" solutions. For example, a new home can be constructed with all entrances on grade, eliminating the need to replace steps with unsightly ramps, and with all living areas on one level, eliminating the need to rely on the operation of lifting equipment on a daily basis. In order to accommodate the additional maneuvering space needed in the bedroom, bathroom, and other areas of the home, the size of the accessible home is much larger than that of a standard two-story or split-level home.

Probable Costs of Modifications

Probable costs are attached to recommended modifications. Probable costs can be obtained from individuals who are familiar with examples of accessible residential modifications, reviews of building cost manuals, discussions with vendors of specialty equipment, and consultations with a remodeling firm. Generally, the costs presented to the client are estimates, especially when the client is looking at the option of purchasing a home and remodeling it rather than remodeling the existing home. Actual costs should be obtained through a competitive bid process after the family has identified a specific housing option.

Depending on the age of the home being modified, additional costs may be necessary to bring operating systems (such as electrical, plumbing, and heating systems) into compliance with current state and local building codes. Specific upgrades and associated costs are not typically reviewed as part of an accessibility evaluation and remain unknown unless the review of the home incorporates an inspection of those items that do not meet current codes. This may require the involvement of a separate building inspector.

In making any modifications, individuals will often retain an architect or accessibility specialist to assist them in ensuring that the modifications designed are appropriate and will accommodate their accessibility needs. Other costs that may impact the total cost are the cost of buying land for the construction of a new home or the cost of purchasing a different home—one that lends itself more easily to modification than the existing home.

The average family moves once every seven years. Depending on the age of the individual with the disability, it is realistic to assume that this individual may move in the future. With each move to a new home, the individual will need the same level of accessibility as that provided by the previous home. If accessibility features are designed to blend with the original structure and are constructed out of quality materials, it is likely that the home will remain attractive for resale, allowing the homeowner to use equity in the home to pay for modifications to the next home. Conversely, if a house is remodeled to look like an institution, it may be difficult to sell, thereby decreasing the homeowner's equity and adding to the probable costs when the person with the disability moves.

CHAPTER 15

DEFENSE'S ANNUITY EXPERT

Mark R. Kosieradzki

Page 223. *Add the following new section after § 15.7:*

§ 15.7A Cross-Examination of the Defense Annuity Expert

The annuity expert is a salesperson, not an economist, an actuary, or a mathematician. The annuitist creates structured settlements by putting together annuity packages that provide a stream of income over a period of years. They act as brokers for various insurance investment vehicles. Many annuitists do this only in the wrongful death and personal injury lawsuit context.

Many annuity experts work exclusively for the defense. Oftentimes insurance companies will refuse to work with an annuitist who has done work with a plaintiff's attorney, in a sense, blackballing a broker that has worked "with the enemy." The National Law Journal, Vol. 17. No. 50, p. A14. Aug. 14, 1995.

The annuitist's job is not complicated. Insurance companies provide the annuitist with a chart (rate book) that outlines their rates. The annuitist merely follows the chart and does the multiplication. This does not constitute expert opinion beyond the mere recitation of a sales quote.

Q. All right, could you describe your business to us in a little more detail? What specifically is your business as an annuitist?
A. We work primarily for the defendants in creating packages in personal injury claims.
Q. When you say "primarily," do you mean 100 percent of your time?
A. Of my time, 100 percent of it is on the defense side, yes, sir.
Q. What do you do for the defendants 100 percent of your time?

* Text of Cross Examination by Thomas A. Demetrio of Corboy and Demetrio in *Dave Allen Rickerson v. H.J. Jeffries Truck Lines* (1983).

A. I work with them to put together packages; when I say "packages," I mean annuity policies to provide stream of income and money in the future to settle personal injury claims.

Q. All right, and that's known in your industry as structured settlements?

A. Yes, that is the generic term for it.

Q. So, you are in the business of structuring settlements?

A. That's correct.

Q. And when you structure a settlement, what do you do?

A. Well, we make an offer to the plaintiff or the injured party of some cash and a stream of income in the future depending on the particular case we try to put it to their needs.

Q. When you say "some cash," what are you saying, purchase the annuity?

A. No, there's usually a combination of some money plus the annuity.

Q. Oh, I see what you are saying, so some money up front?

A. Yes, and then and some money invested in the purchase of an annuity that provides a stream of income, monthly income or annual, an income of some sort in the future.

Q. Using a little imagination you can put together some ingenious packaging, can you not?

A. Well, we can put together a great variety of packaging, yes.

Q. At any rate, you specialize in selling annuity packages to people involved in personal injury cases?

A. That's correct.

Q. In your work as an annuitist, have you ever sold an annuity that did not involve a personal injury or wrongful death matter?

A. No. I don't think so, there's never been one that we have sold that wasn't a personal injury or wrongful death.

Q. And you of course get involved before the trial?

A. Yes.

Q. All right, and after sometimes as well?

A. Yes.

Q. You were contacted in this case on November 7, 1995?

A. I think that's correct.

Q. And Mr. Johnson gave you a breakdown of costs based upon Professor Jordan's work and he asked you to get quotes from various insurance companies and see what premium prices you could come up with in essence?

A. In essence, yes.

Q. All right, when you get a quote from an insurance company, you are getting the premium cost of what it will take to purchase an annuity?

A. That's correct.

Q. And your full time is spent working with insurance carriers that supply those annuities to or quotes for various insurance carriers and defense lawyers?

A. That's correct.

Q. So you went about your task of acquiring what the premium rate would be starting with, let's say, November 7 up until recently to supply a premium of as a matter of fact would parallel the stream of income suggested by Professor Jordan?

A. That's correct.

Q. And you have looked at Exhibit No. 6?

A. Yes.

Q. And would I be accurate in saying that if an individual were to purchase an annuity, he would then in this amount, let's take high school graduate, it says $378,119?

A. Yes.

Q. Am I right? He would have to then take that amount of money and purchase the annuity to actually get the stream of income that you have suggested?

A. Yes, if that $378,119 were paid to the life insurance company today would provide that stream of income as outlined in Mr. Johnson's reports from high school education.

Q. Well, as a matter of fact it would have to be paid to the insurance company in order to get the stream of income?

A. That's correct.

Q. Right?

A. Yes.

Q. In other words those funds would have to be used to purchase the annuity?

A. That's correct.

Q. All right, now, you talked about ABC, am I right?

A. ABC life insurance.

Q. ABC Insurance Company of North America?

A. Correct.

Q. Let's just take them for example, and let's say they have been given this $378,119. That's the premium?

A. That's correct.

Q. The money is in their pocket?

A. Right.

The insurance company recites a price quote and receives a cash payment for the annuity. Very often the annuity broker is not privy to any of the portfolio details on the basis of their quote. The annuitist operates as a broker for the insurance company, merely repeating their premium prices.

Even if the annuitist has knowledge about the details of the portfolio investments, the growth rate offered is only a statement of a small investment vehicle which does not reflect the economy as a whole.

Obviously, the insurance company profits from the sale of the annuity. Generally, the annuitist is not able to disclose, for lack of knowledge, how much the insurance company profits from the sale of an annuity. The low growth rate, coupled with the fact the insurance company profits in an undisclosed amount, takes away from the aboveboard nature of the annuity purchase.

Q. And the insurance company is certainly going to invest that money?
A. Right.
Q. They are not going to let it sit around?
A. I assume so.
Q. And they will be gaining interest on that and hopefully they will be making a profit?
A. Yes.
Q. That's the whole concept?
A. I'm sure they are in business to make a profit.
Q. That's the insurance business, isn't it?
A. Yes.
Q. Like most any other business and let me ask you a question with respect to INA, are you aware of how they invest that money?
A. No, I am not.
Q. Are you aware of the portfolio details of INA?
A. No.
Q. With respect to INA does it supply an annuity at 11 percent growth?
A. Does it supply one? I have never sold one.
Q. How about 10 percent?
A. Again I have never sold one.
Q. How about 9 percent?
A. No, I have never sold one.
Q. Let me ask you this. You have an office downtown?
A. Yes.
Q. You get a phone call from a client, say, Mr. Johnson?
A. Yes.
Q. And then you have to make a phone call?
A. That's right.

Q. Right, and you have to get a base figure from the insurance company?
A. Well, some of their figures I have and I have—and I carry, it's called the rate book and I carry the rate book. If it happens to be something that's not in my rate book, then I have to call the insurance company.
Q. So you have a rate that is for lack of a better expression the bible of your business?
A. So to speak.
Q. Well, your rate book is the most important asset you have as you go around selling annuities?
A. I think so.
Q. And when you look in the rate book you will go, for example, to a 13 year old and then you will go across and there will be a rate?
A. If that's what I'm looking for, I multiply the income, yes.
Q. Let's say that's what you are looking for?
A. All right.
Q. Let's find out from you how if that is the figure in the rate book determined by the insurance company?
A. By the life insurance company?
Q. Yes.
A. I don't know how they determine their rate.
Q. Maybe, I am confusing the issue. Isn't it the life insurance company that supplies that rate in your rate book?
A. Yes.
Q. So how does that insurance company determine rate?
A. I don't know. I just know what the rate is.
Q. So you look at it and they must have a formula of some kind?
A. I'm sure they do. Yes.
Q. And have they shared that with you?
A. No.
Q. Have you an opinion as to why they have not shared that with you?
A. Well, I hate to venture an opinion. I really never asked to have that information because it's not pertinent to me in what I do on a day-to-day operation.
Q. Out of general information has it ever crossed your mind that it would be fun to find out how they get their rates that you rely on?
A. I don't have any feel for how they develop their rates. I know it's a big, successful company and I know they do have rates that they are comfortable with.
Q. As a matter of fact isn't it proprietary?
A. You mean that they would not want to disclose their method for determining the rates?

Q. Yes.
A. I imagine if I ask they will probably tell me it's none of my business. "You are our agent. We will give you our rates and you use them."
Q. So do you know for instance how they determine growth?
A. In what respect?
Q. Any respect?
A. Well, growth in payment, they give me in their rates. In other words I can use, I can determine a certain growth and payout every year by the chart but, but how they determine what they need to develop the growth, I do not know.
Q. All right, and as a matter of fact when you look in your rate book you get a figure per thousand?
A. That's correct.
Q. And then you just do the—I'm not—I'm not suggesting it doesn't take any talent, but you just multiply?
A. It's not very complicated. You are right. No, I just multiply. That's correct.

Insurance companies, like all businesses, are at risk for financial risk and potential bankruptcy. Insolvency creates a substantial risk that the annuity holder will receive a greatly reduced payment and, in some cases, nothing.

Government regulators seized Executive Life Insurance Company of California in 1993. The action slashed the value of thousands of annuities. In some cases annuity holders received less than 50 cents on the dollar. The National Law Journal, Vol. 17 No. 50, p. A14. Aug. 14, 1995.

Q. Now, Mr. McCloud, would you agree with me that the most important aspect of renting out one's money is safety?
A. I think it's a very important aspect, yes.
Q. And certainly in your personal life as well as your professional, that's something that you take into consideration?
A. Yes.
Q. And would you agree generally that a careful investor would want to be concerned with the safety aspect of any investment he or she might make?
A. Yes, I can agree with that.
Q. Now, in this particular business of yours, I think you mentioned there are about 16 life insurance companies that are in your particular stable of companies?

A. That's correct.
Q. And you named a few. Can you name a few more?
A. Well, I'm not sure just which ones I named.
Q. Well, just start over then.
A. Well, there's ABC. . .
Q. Okay.
A. I mean there are probably several others I don't use too often.
Q. Now, do insurance companies sometimes go broke?
A. Insurance companies do sometimes go broke.
Q. Mr. McCloud, in this business of annuities, are there companies that have gone sour so to speak? Gone broke?
A. There's one company that I have heard of that I think is in receivership.
Q. That's XYZ?
A. Yes.
Q. Tell us about XYZ, what it was; wasn't that one of the largest dealers of annuities?
A. Of pensions annuities, not structured settlement annuities.
Q. And what happened to XYZ?
A. Well, as I understand it they are in receivership and being run by the state administrator's operation.
Q. Ever heard of DEF Co.?
A. I have heard of them, yes.
Q. Tell us about that?
A. Well, I'm not an expert on DEF Co. I understand that they—really, I hate to. All I know is what I hear on the T.V. now that there was some fraudulent operations or something as I understand it, but I don't know much about it. I'm sorry.
Q. At any rate if a company takes a premium from an individual and promises to pay "X," then that company has to invest that money presumably at a profit?
A. Yes.
Q. So that stream of income can be given to the individuals over, let's say, a 58-year period of time?
A. Yes.
Q. And that company has to be around to make payments?
A. Yes.
Q. If a company becomes insolvent at a time in the future, there's a problem isn't there?
A. Yes.

Insurance companies receive a rating from the A.M. Best Company. The ratings can change, underscoring the volatility in the insurance industry market.

Q. Now, you mentioned several companies you deal with and you mentioned that the Best people sort of regulate these insurance companies and grade them?
A. Yes, they don't regulate them, but they publish a grade of them, yes.
Q. Okay, and they publish this for people like yourself?
A. Yes, for anybody who wants to buy it from them.
Q. So that when you are dealing and I assume you only deal with A-plus companies?
A. Well, we have a couple of companies rated only A for special situations.
Q. But certainly you would never go down less than an A grade?
A. That's correct.
Q. And of course in your business you have to keep abreast of how these companies are rated?
A. Yes.
Q. You have to know that?
A. Yes, we try to keep abreast of the rating, thats correct.
Q. For instance if ABC on, today, Tuesday November 12th?
A. That's correct.
Q. If ABC was rated A-plus on Monday but today is Tuesday, and now, it would be rated B-plus, you would want to know that?
A. I certainly would.
Q. All right, and that would affect your confidence in ABC, wouldn't it?
A. Yes, it would.
Q. All right, and in this particular lawsuit you had a task that the defense attorney asked you to complete and you checked with ABC?
A. Yes, Number 2 Corporation.
Q. Number 2 Corporation, and Number 3 Corporation, right?
A. Yes.
Q. And all three of them are top rated companies, is that correct?
A. That's correct.
Q. Now, in helping you keep track of the integrity of these insurance companies, do you read the newspaper?
A. Yes, I do.
Q. And do you read like the daily newspaper, the Tribune?

A. Yes, I do.
Q. And they have a business section?
A. Yes.
Q. And you keep track of them?
A. I try to.
Q. Well, it's important to your business that you do, right?
A. Well, I try to keep abreast, yes.
Q. And in this case, you did not hear back from Number 3 Corporation, is that right?
A. I did not get a rating back from them.
Q. And in taking the Chicago Tribune from November 8th, 1995, which was the day after this trial started—you had contacted them before this time, right?
A. Yes.
Q. You contacted them November 8?
A. 7th or 8th.
Q. 7th or 8th?
A. Yes.
Q. At any rate under a big article called, "Annuities," would you agree with this, Number 3 Company," that's what we are talking about, right?
A. Right, I believe that's it, yes.
Q. "The largest firm had its financial stability questioned when its overall rating was dropped to a B-plus rating from an A-plus rating by the by A. M. Best Company, an independent insurance monitoring service."
A. That's a different Number 3 Company.
Q. Pardon me?
A. That's Number 3 Company of New York.
Q. Are they related, sir?
A. Yes, they are in the same holding corporation, but Number 3 Company that I sent my information to is in New Jersey.
Q. But—
A. And it's still A-plus rating.
Q. Aren't they interrelated?
A. Well, the different companies I think are owned by the same parent.
Q. As a matter of fact companies like Merrill Lynch deal in annuities, don't they?
A. Yes, different kinds of annuities.
Q. Well, they don't specialize in your personal injury business?
A. They have pension annuities.
Q. Pardon me?

A. Merrill Lynch buys from life insurance company pension type annuities for pension funds, old age, retirement annuity, that type of thing.
Q. Well, they are all annuities?
A. Yes, they are all annuities.
Q. Pension annuities?
A. That's correct.
Q. It's no different. It supplies a stream of income to an individual when that individual reaches a certain age or that individual reaches a certain point in their employment status?
A. Yes, except there are some differences though.
Q. Pardon me?
A. There are some differences between them.
Q. You mean from the personal injury field?
A. Yes, the annuities that I would purchase from a life insurance company would be somewhat different from the annuities that Merrill Lynch would purchase from a Baldwin or from a Charter Security of New York.

Price quotes on annuity packages traditionally stayed open for 30 days. The 30-day purchase window subsequently was reduced to 15 days, and now, commonly remains open for only 7 days. Price rates and rates of return change constantly, underscoring the uncertainty of the annuity as an indicator of present value.

Q. And is there a life insurance company—an annuity company—that would be willing to take a premium and pay an individual, let's take LPN care, and pay an individual that stream of income needed to meet the cost of that LPN care, so the individual doesn't make a nickel of profit?
A. Yes.
Q. But so that LPN on the 15th and the 30th day of every month gets a paycheck?
A. Yes.
Q. For his or her services, whatever those costs turn out to be, will a company issue an annuity in that amount?
A. Without knowing what the costs are going to be for sure in the future?
Q. That's right?
A. No.
Q. Why not?
A. Because you don't know what you are going to pay.

Q. It would be too risky, wouldn't it?
A. Well, it would be—I don't think it's a matter of risk. I think it's impossible to underwrite.
Q. Well, would you agree with me that some insurance company would not want to take the risk as to what those costs are going to be into the future?
A. Well, there is none that I know of that will. If I understand your questions that will write a policy that will pay the cost, whatever they necessarily might be.
Q. Open ended?
A. Like a medical policy so to speak?
Q. Yes.
A. I don't know of any company. That's more of a health policy and I don't know of any that will write it on a catastrophic injured people.
Q. Let me ask you this. Your Exhibit No. 1, you have certain costs and I guess they total $5,052,669 if it's a high school graduate?
A. Right.
Q. And so an individual would have to take that $5,517,063, go to Chartered Security or INA and say, "Here's your money, guys," and then the stream of income would start?
A. That's the ABC number and, yes, that stream of income will start.
Q. We can assume whether you go to INA or Charter, they are basically going to be about the same aren't they?
A. The format is the same, yes.
Q. Are you suggesting that rates, premiums differ from company to company?
A. Yes, definitely.
Q. Oh, okay, at any rate you selected INA so we will use that.
A. Okay.
Q. This amount that you totalled up, isn't it, sir, just based upon a limited period of time that individual would be able to take this amount of money and purchase the type of stream of income you have testified to here today?
A. Yes, the cost factor is good for 15 days. Is that what you are referring to?
Q. That's what I am referring to, sir.
A. Yes.
Q. So in the next 15 days I'm assuming now you have got these prices current?
A. Those are current.
Q. As of yesterday?
A. They have not changed since November 8th.

Q. Okay, but it's good for 15 days?
A. It's only—yes you can only guarantee that cost at that 15—for 15 days from today.
Q. So on the 16th day this figure may be lower or it may be higher?
A. That's correct.
Q. As a matter of fact these prices fluctuate, don't they?
A. They do fluctuate some.
Q. And can you sit up there and tell us what the costs are going to be in 18 months from now?
A. No.
Q. Twelve months from now?
A. No.
Q. $5,517,063?
A. I can only guarantee you the cost number for 15 days.
Q. By the way, do you and your company that creates these annuity packages, guarantee that the individual is going to get the money that the premium has paid for to supply?
A. Do we guarantee it?
Q. Yes, sir.
A. No.
Q. Do you know, Mr. McCloud, what medical costs have done in the last eight years, what's happened to them?
A. No, not anything more than the general public. They have gone up substantially.
Q. Now, you mentioned that annuities can be split up between different companies, in other words, 25 percent goes to ABC, 25 percent to Number 3, et cetera?
A. Well, we could split it up between different companies, yes.
Q. Well, these are ABC's premium's costs?
A. That's correct.
Q. So you don't know if Number 3 would go along with that?
A. Well, I know that they write it whether they would take exactly one fourth of the premium would be very close.
Q. At any rate, let's just say Number 3 goes broke? All right?
A. Okay.
Q. Let's say that Number 3, that's an A-plus company?
A. Yes, it is.
Q. All right, Number 3 invests money?
A. Yes.
Q. In high-risk investments because they are taking the risk, but they will get more back, wouldn't they?
A. You are suggesting they will make money, I assume, so okay that's correct.

Q. Assume that.
A. Okay.
Q. At any rate they go broke?
A. All right.
Q. All right, in Illinois, isn't there something called the Guarantee Fund?
A. Yes, there is.
Q. And you have told me about that before?
A. I think I did, yes.
Q. So let's tell all of us now the function of the Illinois Fund, Guarantee Fund.
A. Well, I believe the Guarantee Fund is established to insure that some payments are made on an annuity when an insurance company fails, like it's simply stated.
Q. You—
A. Its limited through as I understand.
Q. I know, and you say some payments are made. It's limited to $100,000, isn't it?
A. That's my understanding, yes.
Q. So if a company fails, the individual has the recourse of going to the Guarantee Fund and if things work out at the Guarantee Fund, he can get $100,000, regardless?
A. Yes.
Q. Let's assume it fails when only $1,000,000 has been paid so there is $4,000,000 that hasn't been paid. He only gets $100,000?
A. That's my understanding of it, yes.

CHAPTER 16

THE USE OF NONEXPERT DAMAGES WITNESSES

William D. Harper

Page 238. *Add the following new section after the last paragraph of § 16.2:*

§ 16.3 An SCI Victim's Perspective

Editor's Note: Owen Orthmann suffered a C3-4 injury in an accident at the age of nineteen, resulting in a high-level quadriplegia. Since that time, Mr. Orthmann has developed several devices that allow him to continue to enjoy life.

Mr. Orthmann took a regular crossbow and had it detached from its stock (leaving just the trigger, the rail, and the bow) and mounted on a small steel box that holds an electric solenoid and a pressure sensor switch. The crossbow and the box sit on top of a head from a video camera tripod, and everything sits on a steel frame that attaches to his wheelchair.

When taking aim, Mr. Orthmann uses his chin to move the back end of the bow left, right, up, or down. With the crossbow aimed, he activates an electronic safety switch positioned near his chin and inhales on a tube. The solenoid is powered by the batteries that operate his wheelchair, and the breath of air causes the solenoid to push the trigger and fire the crossbow. The crossbow is equipped with an electronic cocking device, which facilitates target practice.

The following is Mr. Orthmann's description of how he came to make this and other devices that accommodate his disability and the pleasure he derives from them.

I have always felt more comfortable with my disability when I am doing the things I enjoyed doing before my injury. I don't consider myself different from any other able-bodied person. For me, the wheelchair is like a cast on a broken arm; only my adaptations are a little more complex. The following are some of the adaptations that have given me the ability to do some of those things.

I use voice-recognition software to operate a computer at 3M, where I work. Using this computer, I am able to write letters and many other things for which I would normally use a pen and paper. With the Internet growing all the time, I now have access to newspapers, magazines, and endless amounts of information that were previously inaccessible.

My home has been adapted with ramps and a roll-in shower. I chose to modify my home, rather than move, because it is on one level and very open (not full of narrow hallways). I also put a limestone patio in the backyard, which makes it easier to roll my wheelchair through the yard.

For transportation I have an all-wheel-drive minivan. The floor in the cargo area was lowered 4-1/2" and my wheelchair was modified so that I could have plenty of headroom inside. I decided not to install a lift because the space inside the van is limited. Instead, I use a ramp that I had someone build for me. It is made of aluminum and it folds inside the doorway.

I enjoy fishing and have found a way to again spend time on the lake. I bought a pontoon in a kit and my friends helped put it together. The boat was made wider so a wheelchair could fit inside, and a ramp was put on the front for getting the wheelchair on and off the boat. To be able to fish, I diverted power from one of my wheelchair motors to an old wheelchair motor that is used to run a fishing reel. The motor speed is variable, so I can run it fast to set the hook, or slow it down to play a large fish.

My favorite leisure activity has always been bowhunting. I have had a crossbow adapted and spend many hours in the woods each spring and fall. This activity takes much preparation, including making some of the woods wheelchair accessible. I have been fortunate to have had the help of friends and family to accomplish this.

§ 16.3 VICTIM'S PERSPECTIVE

A Quadriplegic Bowhunter Finds a Way

I grew up in northwest Iowa hunting with my family and friends. I enjoyed all types of hunting but, by the time I was sixteen, bowhunting for deer had become my favorite sport. In July 1980, when I was nineteen, a diving accident in the Apple River in Wisconsin left me a high-level quadriplegic, without the use of my arms or legs.

My paralysis did nothing to discourage my bowhunting desires. Even initially, while still in the hospital, I was thinking about ways that a crossbow could be adapted so that I could bowhunt again. It took four or five years of trial and error to build a crossbow that I could take into the woods. This crossbow had many bugs, and it took a few years of modifications to make it a successful weapon. Since that time, I have taken whitetail deer, antelope, and a black bear.

As you can imagine, most of the outdoors is not wheelchair accessible. Finding a good place to hunt is always a big challenge. Typically, I like to hunt in places where farm roads and game trails meet because I can drive my van near them and set up my ground blind with minimal effort. While friends are helping me set up in the ground blind, I leave the van running because the engine noise helps cover any noise we might make as we get ready. Once we are all set, someone will drive the van away for us. Over the years I have found that the animals seem to react as if a farm vehicle came, stopped for a while, and simply drove away.

Because of my high-level injury, I need to have someone nearby while I am hunting. My wife, Heidi, also enjoys bowhunting, and will often sit with me in the same area. This works very well because my motions are limited to a forty-five degree angle. Heidi can cover all the areas I cannot.

We have good friends in western Minnesota with whom we hunt quite often. One friend, Kris, is also disabled, having had arthritis most of his life. The flat terrain of this hunting ground works well for both of us. The Yellow Medicine River runs through this hunting area, and on either side of it lie ten to twenty yards of woods. Dan, our friend who farms the land where we hunt, has set aside twenty yards of the farmland that borders the woods into the Conservation Reserve Program (CRP), a government-subsidized program for protection of the environment. As I understand it, CRP land is usually set aside for periods of ten to twenty years. This arrangement keeps any chemicals from leaching into the river and also keeps Dan's crops from competing with the trees for moisture.

This strip of CRP land creates a unique and accessible hunting opportunity for someone like me, as deer like to come out of the woods and eat at the edge of the crops. Quite often, we will sit in the cornfield and face the woods, or sit in the woods and face the cornfield. When we do see deer, they are within twenty yards.

Dan, Kris, and some of the neighbors have tried to maintain a quality deer management program. They try not to shoot any bucks unless they feel the animals are in the trophy category. On several occasions they have let small bucks walk right into their stand just to get an opportunity to shoot a doe. This has increased the number of adult deer seen in the area. In 1994 Heidi shot her first deer, which happened to be a trophy buck. Over the years, Dan and Kris have also shot trophies.

The bucks are always more visible and huntable as the peak of the rut approaches. During that peak, the weather is usually cold enough that my disability does not allow me to hunt. So in all my years of hunting from my wheelchair I have never seen a trophy-class buck.

One evening in late October 1995, Dan took time off from his farm work to help Heidi and me get set up in a river-crossing blind that we like to hunt. The blind, located not more than a couple of hundred yards from the back of his barn, is a very difficult place to hunt (because the deer will bed down there during the day, it is very hard to get into the woods without disturbing them), but we decided to go there anyway.

Sure enough, as we drove into the blind, we chased away several deer that had been bedded down in the woods. We felt we probably had greatly decreased our chances of seeing deer. But we knew we did not have enough time left in the day to go to another blind, so we decided to hunt there anyway. Once Heidi and I were in place, Dan drove our van away and said he would be back to pick us up at dark.

The wind was very light that night so the woods were still and quiet. Most of the leaves had already fallen off the trees, so we had good vision across the river and through the woods to the fields.

As expected, hunting was slow that evening; we saw birds, squirrels, and nothing else until ten minutes before dark. At that time, I spotted a raccoon wandering up from the river. It stood about thirty yards in front of me.

For several years Dan had told us about his raccoon problem and had encouraged us to help him out if we had the opportunity. Since our hunt was basically over, I decided this would be a chance to test my accuracy and give Dan one more fur to sell. I took aim and fired. The shot was perfect.

Heidi laid down her bow to turn and walk a couple of yards to see what I had shot. We watched the raccoon run a short distance before it fell to the ground. As I was whispering to Heidi, telling her the details, she looked over her shoulder and said she saw a deer just coming into the woods about 75 yards away. I was slightly sick: I had taken my only shot, and reloading my bow would make too much noise and scare the deer. Heidi's bow was on the ground behind us. We figured the deer would never be closer to us before dark. "The deer is heading our way," she said, "and I think it's a buck."

Now I felt less sick, because this would surely be another small buck, which we would not shoot anyway. We would get to watch this little buck as we waited to be picked up by Dan.

"I think he might be a shooter," Heidi said as she counted the points. "Seven, eight, nine. He's a ten-pointer and definitely a trophy."

"You've got to be full of it," I said, not wanting to believe her.

"No, I'm not kidding at all. Look over your left shoulder and you'll be able to see him in a second," she whispered.

She wasn't kidding or exaggerating at all. This was a very nice ten-pointer and he was walking on a trail that would eventually put him directly in front of me at 25 yards.

The buck was totally unaware of us and would have been as easy a shot as I have ever had. Mother Nature had him full of hormones and safety was not one of his priorities.

I whispered to Heidi, "See if you can get to your bow by using me as your cover." Heidi managed to get to her bow, but the buck caught some slight movement that drew his attention in our direction. We froze as he stared at us and slowly started moving away from our blind. When he was facing the opposite direction, I made a grunting sound with my mouth. At this, the buck turned and came closer to us. We repeated the sound several times, but we could never get him close enough for Heidi to get a shot. The original movement he had picked up kept him from coming closer. I think that if we had a decoy set up, this buck would have worked it over well.

A couple of minutes later Dan drove up and I was forced to tell him about the trophy raccoon that we had just gotten. Since that night I have been the butt of many jokes, and I am sure I will never hear the end of it. For my buddies and me, hunting is more than just shooting trophies. Mainly it's about being with friends, sharing stories,and—sometimes—receiving nicknames. I have a feeling I earned a new one (perhaps several new ones) that night.

The State Record That I Caught With My Chin

After my spinal cord injury, and after several years of trial and error, my buddies and I devised a way for me to go fishing again. We modified my power wheelchair so that the motor that drives my chair also cranks my reel. The rig works great. I can give it a lot of speed to set the hook or I can back off and play the fish if it is big. As I am not able to cast the pole, I bobber fish and sometimes troll.

Last July, three friends and I decided to go for a leisurely pontoon ride on Forest Lake. I wanted to fish, so we got some sucker minnows and went to a hot spot where I thought we could catch some pike. Northern fishing was slow so the others decided to try for panfish. Toward the end of the evening we decided to move to an area where a small stream empties into the lake. Early in the season we had had good luck catching panfish at this spot, but in July the area was looking pretty scummy. The shoreline was full of lily pads and the water was like green malt. However, we decided to try it for a few minutes before heading in.

I had one friend cast my sucker near the edge of the lily pads, hoping "Mr. Big Bass" would be hanging out waiting to take my line for a run. The bobber and sucker landed on top of the lily pads and in order to get it where I wanted it, I had to reel in just a bit. I knew the sucker was fresh by the way the bobber started jumping when the sucker fell off the lily pads. Just when I was about convinced this was the liveliest sucker I had ever seen, the bobber suddenly disappeared. I waited a few seconds and then set the hook quickly. The fish pulled a lot of drag off the reel. We knew this had to be a giant bass or something bigger, and after battling awhile I was able to pull it up enough where we could see it was long and thin. As it was smothered with weeds, we could not see it well. We assumed it was a big pike or a Muskie. Eventually, when I got the fish up to the boat, it started rolling, boiling up the surface of the water. One friend finally got the net under the whole mess and lifted it out of the water.

Just then the fish let out a loud "GGRRRRRRRR," and I realized I had just caught the biggest, ugliest, nastiest dogfish I had ever seen. As soon as my friend laid the fish on the deck, the others fled to the opposite side of the boat and did not want to come near it. After a great deal of coaxing and begging, I convinced one friend to weigh the ugly beast. The fish weighed 11 pounds and 1 ounce.

After more coaxing and begging, my friends put the dogfish on a stringer and we hauled it back to the marina to show it to another friend. Our friend was gone, but several kids from the campground ran over to see the fish we brought in. Not knowing what to do with it, we gave it to the kids, who acted as if Christmas had arrived in the middle of July.

On our drive back to the city I couldn't help wondering how big a dogfish can actually grow. I could not remember anyone catching one weighing over 5 or 6 pounds. The next day, we looked at the Minnesota regulations to see what the state record was. To our surprise, the record was held by a fish that weighed 10 pounds and 15 ounces. We had given away the state record dogfish to a bunch of kids.

Later we found out the kids' parents made them throw the fish back in the lake. So all I am left with is a picture and the memory of a great battle that my fishing rig and I eventually won.

CHAPTER 17

BIOMECHANICS OF INJURY

by James R. Pratt III

§ 17.1 Anatomy of Spine
§ 17.2 Application of Engineering Principles
§ 17.3 Mechanism of Spinal Cord Injury
§ 17.4 Use of a Biomechanical Expert
§ 17.5 Qualifying the Biomechanical Engineer
§ 17.6 Variety of Uses for the Biomechanical Expert's Expertise
§ 17.7 Conclusion

§ 17.1 Anatomy of Spine

In order to understand the biomechanics of injury, one must understand basic concepts about the anatomy of the spine.

Essentially, the spine is the skeleton's main load-bearing member for the mid-section of the body and is represented by cylinders of bone stacked upon each other and bound together by ligaments between each part of cylinders. Each of these bony cylinders provides some shield or protection from the spinal cord and nerves that are attached to the spinal cord. There are numerous ligaments, muscles, and joints between these cylinders that allow flexing and mobility. The spinal cord itself is the nerve connection from the brain to the remainder of the body. It is about an inch in diameter and about 16 to 18 inches long. The cord itself does not travel the entire length of the spinal canal but instead ends at approximately level Lumbar 1 or Lumbar 2. The spine is a flexible, segmented, load-bearing conduit for the spinal cord and nerves. It is categorized in five groups from the head downward in terms cervical, thoracic, lumbar, sacral, and coccygeal vertebrae. Alvin, S. Hyde, Crash Injuries: How and Why They Happen, Ch. 9 (1992).

Figure 17-1 shows the four groups of vertebrae and their curvatures and demonstrates that there are seven cervical vertebrae, twelve thoracic vertebrae, and five lumbar vertebrae. **Figure 17-2** shows the relationship between the spinal cord and the spinal nerves that attach to the cord. **Figure 17-3** utilizes a lumbar vertebrae showing the basic component part of the vertebrae.

With this basic anatomy in mind, it is easy to see that spinal cord injuries occur primarily when there is a disruption or impingement of the spinal cord and/or nerves attached to the spinal cord. Since the spinal cord is the primary pathway of nerve impulses from the brain to the other portions of the body, the disruption of this nerve pathway causes a loss of function below the level of the disruption. Hence, the most important thing to understand concerning biomechanics is how trauma causes disruption of the nerve pathways and/or impingement or disruption of the spinal cord.

§ 17.2 Application of Engineering Principles

Essentially, the safety of any structure is determined by its weakest link and a failure of the structure occurs when an external load stresses the body beyond a level that the body can tolerate. Typically this load causes a person to be struck by a moving mass or to be stopped very quickly by a stationary mass. The time over which the load is applied, as well as how quickly a person is stopped when encountering some object, determines to a great degree whether there will be an injury and the severity of an injury. Stress occurring in the human body and response to external forces depends on the speed at which the force is applied and how that stress is distributed. The science of biomechanics is the application of engineering principles to the body, helping scientists understand human tolerance and injury mechanisms.

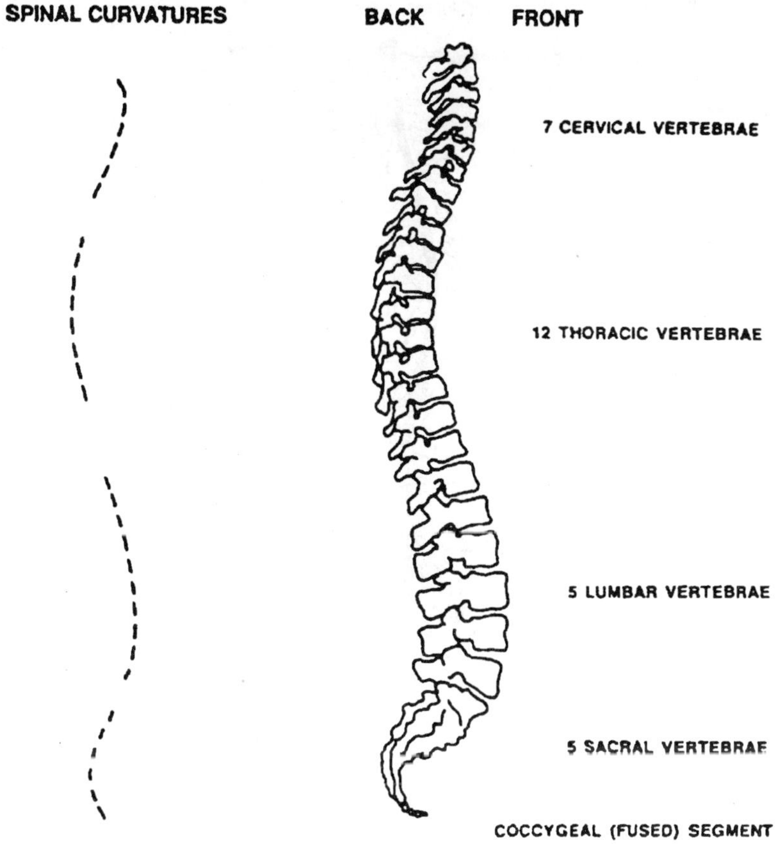

This simple drawing identifies the grouping of vertebrae into 7 cervical, 12 thoracic, 5 lumbar and 5 sacral (fused) vertebrae, with the somewhat vestigial four or so coccygeal vertebrae located at the very bottom of the vertebral column, as a forward facing projection.

The serpentine curvatures reverse at each group of vertebrae. As viewed from in back of the individual, we see a cervical concavity, a thoracic convexity, a lumbar concavity and a sacral convexity. These charming curves are readily deformable into the poor postures we often see.

The cervical and lumbar curvatures are considered to be secondary curves in that they do not develop until we stand up and walk.

Figure 17-1. Four groups of vertebrae and their curvatures.

Source: Reprinted with permission from Hyde, A. *Crash Injuries: How and Why They Happen*, ©1992 Hyde Associates, Inc. For more information, please call (305) 361-5900.

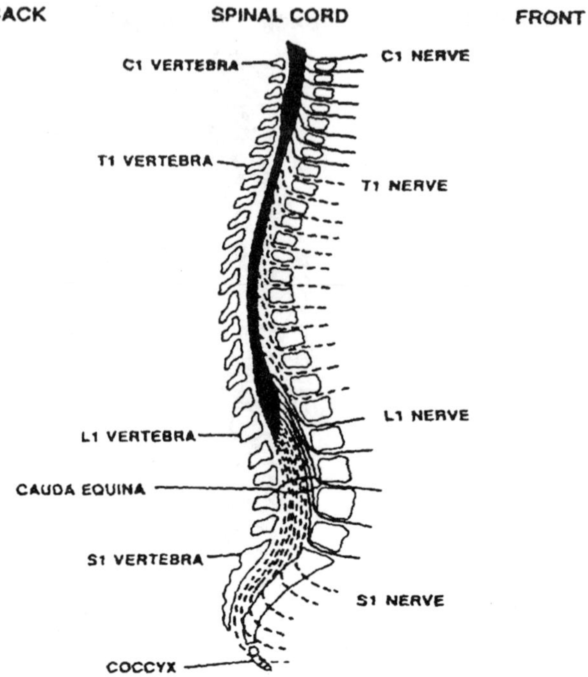

This view is a vertical slice through the middle of the spine and the spinal cord (i.e., through the median plane). Note that:

1) only at Cl do the nerves emerge at about the same level that there are appropriate foramina for them to emerge through;
2) the spinal cord ends at about LI/L2;
3) there are 2 dilatations of the spinal cord, the first from about C2 to about C6 (spinal segments C4 to TI), the second from about Tll to L2 (spinal segments L2 to 53). The upper dilatation accommodates the extra innervation of the brachial plexus for the upper limbs; the lower dilatation accommodates the innervation for the lumbar and sacral plexuses supplying the lower limbs;
4) because the bony spine has grown so much more than did the spinal cord, the lower lumbar and sacral nerves emerge from the bony spine a very great distance from where they first emerged from the spinal cord itself.

Figure 17-2. The relationship between the spinal cord and the foramina through which the spinal nerves emerge.

Source: Reprinted with permission from Hyde, A. *Crash Injuries: How and Why They Happen*, ©1992 Hyde Associates, Inc.

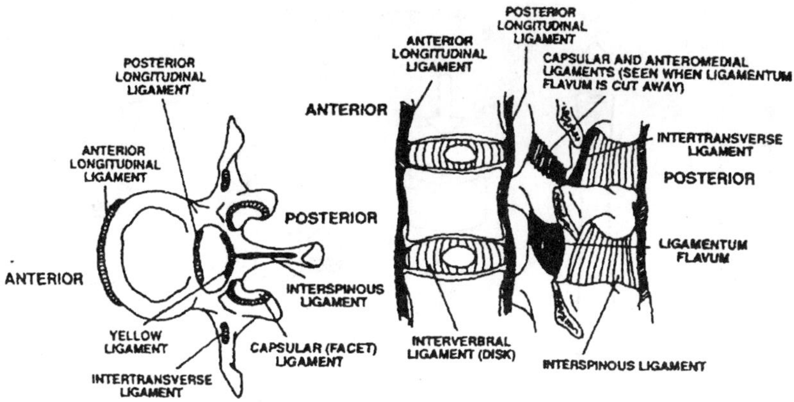

Figure 17-3. Lumbar vertebrae and the ligaments that join them together, especially the intervertebral disc.

Source: Reprinted with permission from Hyde, A. *Crash Injuries: How and Why They Happen*, ©1992 Hyde Associates, Inc.

It is also helpful to understand the directions of force that cause injury. **Figure 17-4** shows directions of forces that tear apart (in this case, the concept of a cylinder is used so as to apply that to the spinal cord later in the chapter). As you can see, the tension is the pulling apart of the cylinder, with compression being pushing both ends towards each other. Torsion is rotation and shear is the horizontal application of force in opposite directions. **Figure 17-5** shows bending forces which are the application of both tension and compression to the cylinder, as well as compression and torsion combined. **Figure 17-6** shows the resulting typical fracture patterns in a cylinder or bone as a result of these forces. **Figure 17-7** is a demonstration of the basic directions of movement for the human head and neck, as well as at the bottom the application of the basic forces as they would be applied to the bony cylinders or vertebrae of the spine.

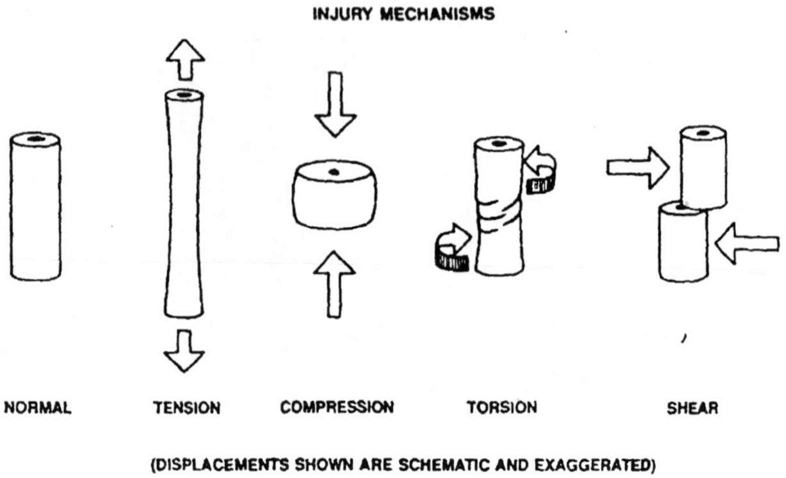

This illustration shows a viscoelastic thick-walled cylinder subjected to *all* of the possible directions by which force may be applied to it. The forces being exerted here are called *stresses.*

The responses of the cylinder here are both exaggerated and schematic, in the name of clarity. The response to the forces/stresses are displacements, and we call them *strains.*

I hope that these simple stresses and the resultant strains are *very clear* to you, because they are, in large part, the basis of understanding how and why we break and tear the way we do.

TENSION = to pull apart
COMPRESSION = to push together
TORSION = to twist (or wring)
SHEAR = to slide apart (in opposite but parallel directions)

Strain is the displacement that is caused by a stress.

Figure 17-4. Directions of the force that tear us apart.

Source: Reprinted with permission from Hyde, A. *Crash Injuries: How and Why They Happen*, ©1992 Hyde Associates, Inc.

BENDING FORCE APPLIED
TO THICK WALLED CYLINDER (SEE TEXT)

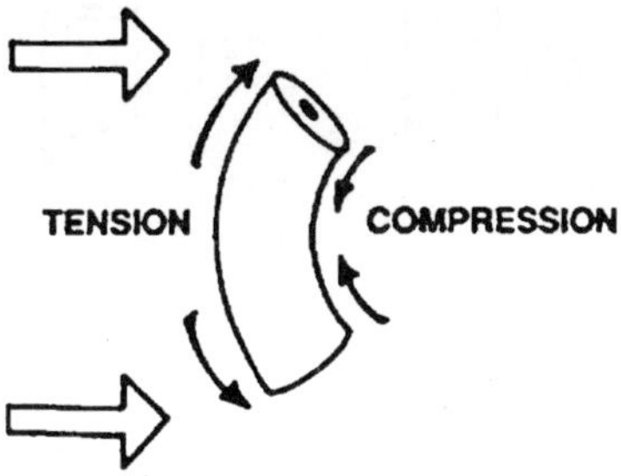

BENDING FORCES

Long bones, such as our thigh bones, will not infrequently be fractured by bending forces.

This illustration is intended to show that bending, as applied to a thick walled cylinder (or a long bone), is made up of tension on one side of the cylinder and of compression on the other side of the cylinder.

COMBINED TORSION AND COMPRESSION
APPLIED TO THICK WALLED CYLINDER

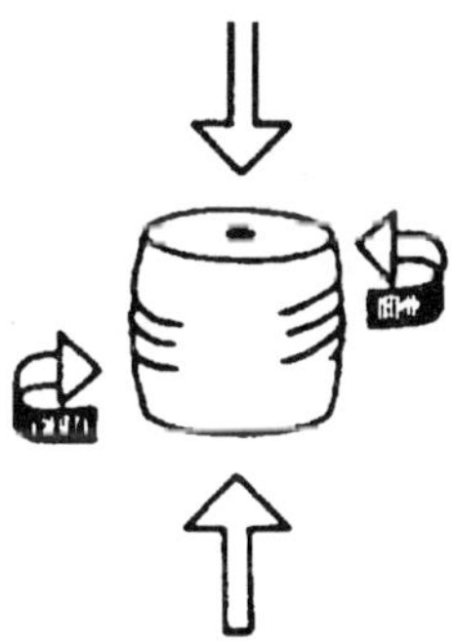

This illustrates that any number of forces (stresses) may be applied together to cause a combination of displacements (strains) that would not ordinarily occur *unless* they were caused by combined stresses.

The lesson to be learned here is that unusual and extraordinary fractures and tears of softer tissues should cause us to seek unusual and extraordinary combinations of forces that could have caused them.

Figure 17-5. Compression and torsion combined and applied to a thick walled cylinder.

Source: Reprinted with permission from Hyde, A. *Crash Injuries: How and Why They Happen*, ©1992 Hyde Associates, Inc.

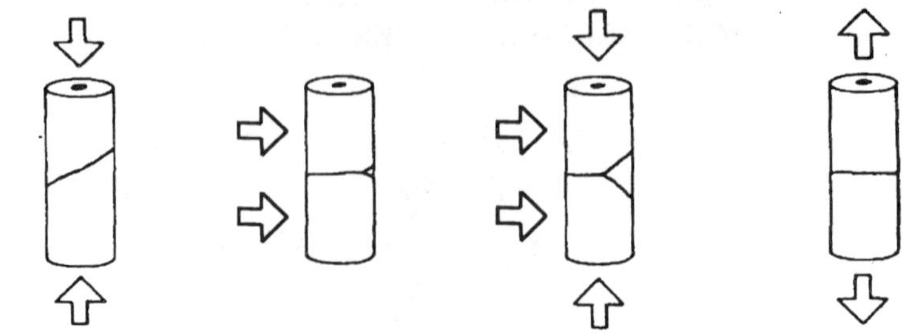

By subjecting a long bone (femur, humerus, tibia, etc.) to some of the stresses typical of crashes we may see characteristic fracture patterns in the long bone.

Note the *oblique* fracture shown above due to compression, the *transverse* fracture with what is termed a *butterfly fragment* at the convex side that results from bending (and a typically much larger version of the butterfly fragment that results from combined bending and compression). Simple tension causes a purely *transverse* fracture, seen in the right side of this rather idealized representation of long bone fractures.

Fracture patterns generally are so characteristic of the forces (stresses) that caused them that they usually permit us to define the directions of the force(s) that caused them.

You may also want to consider that a fracture is simply a strain (displacement) caused by a stress (force) that exceeded the *elasticity* of the material of which the long bone is composed. In a sense, this is not unlike subjecting a rubber band (a very elastic material) to progressive tension (i.e., stretching the rubber band) until the rubber band's elastic limit was exceeded, which is to say that the rubber band was stretched until it broke.

Figure 17-6. Typical fracture patterns in the midportion of a long bone.

Source: Reprinted with permission from Hyde, A. *Crash Injuries: How and Why They Happen*, ©1992 Hyde Associates, Inc.

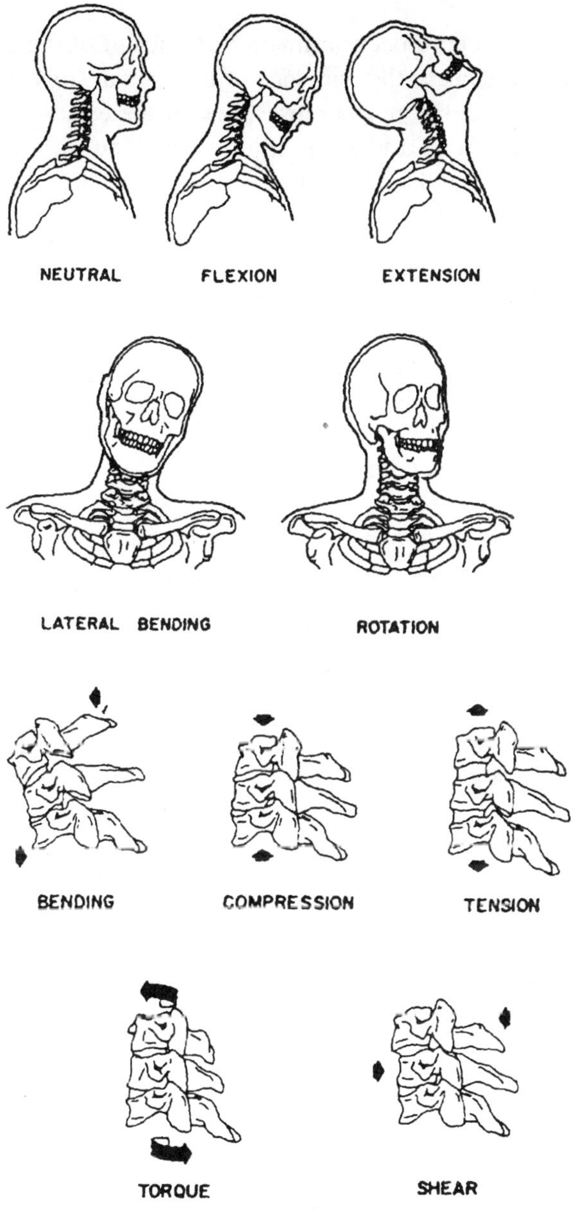

Figure 17-7. Basic directions of movement for the human head and neck.

Source: Reprinted with permission from *Accidental Injury Biomechanics & Prevention,* Nahum, A.M. and Melvin, J.W. eds., © 1993 by Springer-Verlag, New York, N.Y.

§ 17.3 Mechanism of Spinal Cord Injury

Injuries to the spinal cord occur primarily as a result of the combination of movement that exceeds the tolerance of the human spine or loads that exceed that tolerance. For our purposes, one of the easiest ways to consider these injuries is to divide the injuries into the different types of loads that are applied and to examine the effect those loads have on various parts of the spine.

Compression

You will recall that compression is the application of force in an axial (straight line) direction as if the force is being applied from top towards the bottom of the vertebral column. Compression injuries can cause cervical, lumbar, or thoracic injuries.

Purely compressive loading of the cervical spine does not occur frequently but can result in various types of fractures. One of the best known is a Jefferson burst fracture as shown in **Figure 17-8** These typically occur in the upper cervical region. Lower cervical compression injuries occur at all vertebral levels from C-2 to T-1 and typically result at C-4, C-5, and C-6 with loss of disc height.

Injuries can also occur in compression as a result of a combination of compression and flexion. These typically are called wedge fractures, burst fractures, or anterior dislocation, as demonstrated in **Figure 17-9**.

Compression extension fractures can also occur and this type of loading produces fractures of the posterior elements of the cervical spine.

Likewise, tension injuries can occur as a result of pure tension, although this type of injury seems to occur mostly in the upper cervical spine or they can occur as a result of a combination of the tension extension or tension flexion. Examples of tension extension would be whiplash injury or a hanging. This type of injury is demonstrated in **Figure 17-10**.

Injuries can also occur as a result of compression, combined with flexion or extension. Typically, the combination of compression and flexion results in wedge fractures, burst fractures, or anterior dislocation while compression extension fractures produce damage to the posterior element of the cervical spine. An example of a compressive fracture could be a roof case in which the occupant strikes the roof without the

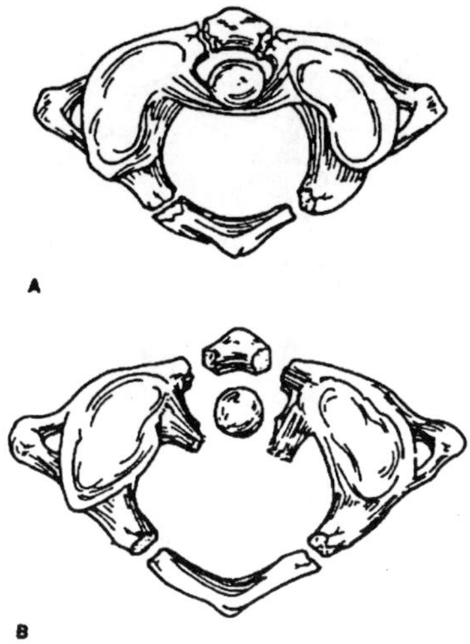

Figure 17-8. Jefferson burst fracture of the atlas vertebra. (From Gallie et al., 1989.).

Source: Reprinted with permission from *Accidental Injury Biomechanics & Prevention,* Nahum, A.M. and Melvin, J.W. eds., © 1993 by Springer-Verlag, New York, N.Y.

head flexed so that the load is axial or directly through the vertebral column as opposed to a bending of the column.

Flexion

As mentioned above, a combination of compression and flexion can result in wedge fractures, burst fractures, or anterior dislocation. These injury patterns are demonstrated in **Figure 17-9**.

Flexion can be thought of as chin-to-chest and is often referred to as hyperflexion when it causes injury. In essence, the head flexes forward to the point where there is a dislocation between two vertebrae with the facets of the one of the vertebrae typically moving over and locking in place above the other vertebrae. This is referred to as either unilateral or bilateral locked facets. In a pure flexion injury, the resulting condition is bilateral locked facets which impinge on the cord, causing a loss of function below the level of the impingement. An example of a flexion injury would be a roof crush case in which the occupant's head contacts the roof in a flexed position where it is held in place with the upper torso and body continuing to move relative to the head causing hyperflexion

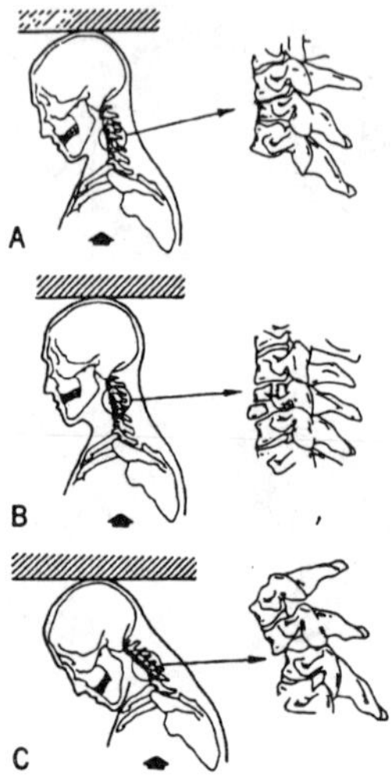

A. Wedge fractures.
B. Burst fracture.
C. Anterior dislocation.

Figure 17-9. Flexion-compression injury mechanisms.

Source: Reprinted with permission from *Accidental Injury Biomechanics & Prevention,* Nahum, A.M. and Melvin, J.W. eds., © 1993 by Springer-Verlag, New York, N.Y.

and typically the bilateral locked facets' dislocation. A similar result often obtains in a seat back failure case where the occupant's head and neck strikes the rear seat and is stopped with the upper torso continuing to move rearward causing a dislocation.

Distraction

Distraction is the shearing or separation of the column typically wherein a portion of the column moves horizontally in one direction with the lower portion moving in the opposite direction. An example of this type of injury could be a door-mounted restraint system wherein the occupant contacts the shoulder harness and the head and neck are stopped while the torso continues to move, sometimes causing a distraction or separation of the column.

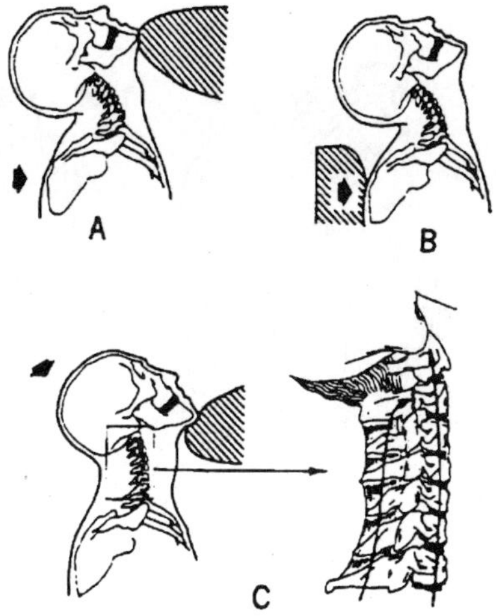

Figure 17-10. Tension-extension injury mechanisms.

Source: Reprinted with permission from *Accidental Injury Biomechanics & Prevention,* Nahum, A.M. and Melvin, J.W. eds., © 1993 by Springer-Verlag, New York, N.Y.

Extension

Extension injuries are less common and often occur in combination with closed-head injuries. For example, in a vehicle that had no head restraint and is rear-ended, a pure extension injury could occur either in combination with a head injury or without a head injury.

Miscellaneous

Tension injuries can occur as a result of pure tension, although this type of injury seems to occur mostly in the upper cervical spine, or can occur as a result of the combination of tension extension or tension flexion. An example of tension extension would be whiplash or hanging. This type of injury is demonstrated in **Figure 17-10**. A combination of tension and flexion can also result in bilateral facet dislocation as demonstrated in **Figure 17-11**.

Injury can also be produced as a result of torsion (rotation) or lateral bending or shear or some combination of those directional forces; however, these injuries are less frequent. James H. McElhaney & Barry S. Myers, *Biomechanical Aspects of Cervical Trauma, in Accidental Injury*

NORMAL FACETS DIRECTION OF FORCE BILATERAL LOCKED FACETS

As shown here the facets of the upper vertebra not only dislocated forward to be on top of the facets of the lower vertebra ("*perched*"), they continued to slide forward until they dropped in front of and *locked* against the facets of the vertebra below them. When they were perched on top of the lower vertebra's superior facets they were termed "perched" facets. This injury of course cannot occur unless there has been extensive disruption of the intervertebral ligaments, which lead us to expect that this dislocation is unstable.

As the arrow above indicates, this dislocation results from a considerable force exerted and directed both upward and forward.

Unilateral facet dislocations also are most common in the lower cervical vertebrae, where the facets form about a 45-degree angle to the horizontal.

Figure 17-11. Bilateral Perched and Locked Facets.

Source: Reprinted with permission from Hyde, A. *Crash Injuries: How and Why They Happen*, ©1992 Hyde Associates, Inc.

Biomechanics and Prevention (Alan M. Nahum & John W. Melvin eds., 1993).

Types of Fractures

Injuries to the spine typically fall within one of the following areas:

1. Anterior wedge fractures of vertebral bodies.
2. Burst fractures of vertebral bodies.

3. Dislocations and fracture dislocations.
4. Rotational injuries.
5. Chance fractures.
6. Hyperextension injuries.
7. Soft tissues injuries.

Anterior wedge fractures can occur at all levels of the spine but are most likely between T-12 and L-2, although they have been demonstrated to occur between T-4 and T-6.

Another type of injury is the burst fracture which is typically an applied force directly over the vertebral body that causes that body to break into two or more segments with the spinal cord being threatened by the movement of the segments into the canal.

Dislocations and fracture dislocations are usually flexion injuries accompanied by rotation and shear. Oftentimes the dislocation causes the facets to jump over and lock on the adjacent vertebral body causing the cord to be subjected to shearing and stretching forces.

Rotational injuries can occur if the spine is twisted about its longitudinal axis and subjected to shearing forces.

There is an injury called the *chance fracture* which is a lap belt related syndrome in which a lumbar vertebrae is split when the lumbar spine flexes over the belt causing separation of the posterior elements.

Hypertension injuries that result in a fracture are sometimes referred to as tear drop fractures. Albert I. King, *Injury to the Thoraco-Lumbar Spine and Pelvis, in Accidental Injury Biomechanics and Prevention* (Alan M. Nahum & John W. Melvin eds., 1993).

§ 17.4 Use of a Biomechanical Expert

Biomechanical engineers have the expertise and background necessary to provide essential testimony concerning injury causation. For a number of years, these engineers have been used in crashworthiness cases to establish the link between a defective design and an enhanced injury. Biomechanical engineers have also been called upon to testify in favor of or against seat belt defenses. The purpose of this paper is to demonstrate the continued viability of the biomechanical engineer's testimony in these areas and to suggest that the biomechanical engineer can provide meaningful and important testimony not only concerning injury causation but in confirmation of both accident reconstruction and the severity of injury under a variety of circumstances.

§ 17.5 Qualifying the Biomechanical Engineer

The single most important point to consider when qualifying the biomechanical expert is the necessity of establishing that biomechanical engineering is not "junk science." It is, therefore, important to stress that biomechanics is a science combining the expertise of both medicine and engineering. It is helpful if the jury can understand that "biomechanics is nothing but the study of the principles of the action of forces and their effects. It is involved in processes causing traumas, in trauma management, in physiology, in pathology, in recovery, in physical therapy, in rehabilitation, in the design of vehicles, and in personal protection." Y.C. Fung, *The Biomechanics of Trauma*, "The Application of Biomechanics to the Understanding an Analysis of Taume," pp. 1–16 (Alan M. Nahum & John Melvin eds. 1985). This science has a long and well-accepted historical basis. Research has been ongoing since the second decade of the 20th century and has resulted in

> impact injury prevention through the application of biomechanics to protective design of transportation vehicles; the stress analysis of men, both static and dynamic, to evaluate reversible and irreversible limits for combinations of mechanical force variables; the development of human surrogate dummies for product performance testing; improved analysis of accidental injury data by comparison with experimental criteria; and a body of knowledge to verify rules and standards for safety requirements in production of transportation vehicles.

John P. Stapp, *Impact Injury of the Head and Spine*, "Historical Review of Impact Injury and Protection Research," pp. 31–32 (Channing L. Ewing, M.D. et at. eds. 1983). In fact, the Committee to Review the Status and Progress of Injury Control Programs at the Centers for Disease Control has opined,

> future historians will mark this (the Center for Injury control) as the turning point for injury control, when science begins defining injury, measuring determinants, devising interventions, and implementing control. It will also be seen as a cooperative effort when social norms changed and

> the public demanded protection from unsafe products or drunk drive[r]s, as well as a time when politicians in government were willing to provide leadership.

William H. Foege, *Injury Control: A Review of the Status and Progress of the Injury Control Program at the Centers for Disease Control,* National Academy Press, Washington, D.C., 1988, p. vi.

The Committee to Review the Status and Progress of the Injury Control Program defined injury biomechanics as "research [which] addresses the mechanisms of physical and physiologic responses to impact, including that of penetrating and nonpenetrating blows to the body. Knowledge of the biomechanics of injury helps to provide the basis for designing less injurious products and environments." Committee to Review the Status and Progress of the Injury Control Program at the Centers for Disease Control, *Injury Control: A Review of the Status and Progress of the Injury Control Program at the Centers for Disease Control,* National Academy Press, Washington, D.C., 1988, p. 11. Thus, there is a clear basis in fact and science establishing the credibility and authenticity of biomechanics. The science relied upon by this specialty involves the principles of physics, engineering (mechanics), biology, anatomy, physiology, and various medical specialties. A clear understanding of the background and the training of the biomechanical engineer not only aids in qualification but helps establish this expert's role in the analysis of a given accident.

Traditional Legal Rules Apply

There are not many cases that have examined the qualifications of biomechanical engineers to testify as experts on injury causation. Typically, a biomechanical engineer is viewed by the courts as simply another expert whose testimony is either accepted or rejected based upon the background of the expert, the basis for the expert's testimony, and the need for expert testimony on that issue. For example, in *Mannino v. International Mfg. Co.*, 650 F.2d 846 (6th Cir. 1981), the court allowed the testimony of a biomechanical engineer under Federal Rules of Evidence 702 and 703, finding that the expert's reliance upon his own studies, his own experience and testing, and the literature generally utilized by such experts had an adequate basis for his testimony. However, in *Breeden v. Valencial, Inc.*, 557 So. 2d 302 (La. Ct. App.), *writ denied,*

558 So. 2d 607 (La. 1990), the court rejected the testimony of a biomechanical engineer based upon the expert's lack of experience with the type of incident that occurred and the product in question. In *Church v. Martin-Baker Aircraft Co.*, 643 F. Supp. 499 (E.D. Mo. 1986), the court rejected the testimony of a biomechanical engineer based upon the expert's lack of experience with the type of injury received. Based upon these examples, it is clear that the courts have not rejected the science of biomechanical engineering, but instead look to the mainstream of medical science to improve the expert's standing in the eyes of the jury. In the appropriate case, it also qualifies this expert to talk about the cost of injury.

§ 17.6 Variety of Uses for the Biomechanical Expert's Expertise

The following discusses four different ways that a biomechanical engineer can be used in looking at the issue of causation. The first two of these are the most traditional. We have certainly seen an increase in the use of the seat belt defense, particularly given increased usage of seat belts by occupants and increased public acceptance of the seat belt. In crashworthiness cases, there has been a long-standing need for an expert that could tie a particular defect to injury causation and address the issue of injury enhancement. Additional consideration will be given to utilizing the biomechanical expert to determine occupant kinematics that helps establish the defect and to confirm the reconstruction of the accident through the use of biomechanics.

Seat Belt Defense

The seat belt defense is being seen with increased frequency, particularly in states with mandatory usage laws, and, in crashworthiness cases, the argument that failure to use the seat belt is a misuse of the product or an assumption of the risk is a common defense. Therefore, lawyers need to be able to address whether or not the occupant was utilizing the seatbelt, as well as the more important issue of whether the seat belt would have made any difference.

In approaching the issue of whether an occupant is belted, it is essential that the practitioner understand how seat belts work and how they protect occupants during a crash. It is fundamental physics that when a car crashes an occupant stays in motion unless acted upon by a restraint system. Thus, the occupant moves in a direction opposite to the direction of the crash forces. For example, if the occupant is the driver and his/her vehicle is struck from the passenger side in a side impact, the occupant will move towards the passenger side unless restrained. Given these basic laws of physics and an understanding of the human tolerance to injury, a biomechanical engineer can examine the seat belt and the interior of the vehicle in question to determine whether there are marks on the belt indicating that the belt locked during an accident event or, alternatively, witness marks within the vehicle where the occupant struck some portion of the vehicle. If occupant contact marks are found at a location where the occupant would not be expected to make contact, this is an indication that either the belt did not work or that it was not being utilized. Likewise, loading marks on the belt may well establish that the belt was being utilized at the time of an incident. Another alternative approach involves the examination of medical records and interviews with the client to establish whether or not there were bruises or other indicators of contact with the belt on the occupant upon initial medical examination which would help to establish belt usage. Abdominal bruising (caused by a lap belt) or upper torso bruising (caused by a shoulder harness) consistent with belt usage may well defeat any claim that the belt was not being utilized. It should be remembered that while evidence of loading on the belt and evidence of occupant contact with the belt is extremely helpful, there is an increasing frequency with which seat belts simply do not work. I have seen individual cases where a retractor failed to lock completely or was delayed in locking. Likewise, I have seen cases where the belt failed to lock initially and the occupant makes a substantial contact with the interior of the vehicle before the belt can lock, resulting in an absence of marking both on the occupant and the belt. Consideration should be given to the fact that not all belts perform the same and the seat belts perform differently given different types of accidents. Thus, the determination as to whether a biomechanical expert can solve the question of belt usage depends upon the type of accident; the dynamics of the collision; the type of belt system design being utilized; the injuries sustained by the occupant; and the forensic evidence available for analysis.

Tying Injury Causation to Defect

I am going to use two examples in pointing out the potential for biomechanical testimony in tying the specific defect to the injury. First, consider the situation where a vehicle rolls over and an occupant is rendered a quadriplegic as the result of alleged defects in the design of the roof. For purposes of this case analysis, assume that there are three average-size males in the front seat of a vehicle and the vehicle has approximately four inches of head space for these occupants. During the rollover sequence and roof crush, the roof crushes ten inches in a "V" shape down the middle, and the occupant in the middle is paralyzed as a result of injury to his spine at the T-8 level. Given this set of facts, the biomechanical expert would examine medical records, x-rays, the subject vehicle, and any testing that has been done by the manufacturer to determine whether or not the occupant sustained injury when the roof crushed. Typically, the manufacturer uses the defense or argument that the occupant dove into the roof and sustained classic diving-type injuries. For purposes of this example, let's assume that the occupants were all unbelted. In this particular accident, it is possible for a biomechanical engineer to review videotapes of drop tests done by the manufacturer which dramatically illustrate that the roof crushes in and contacts the occupant prior to the occupant diving into the roof. Additionally, medical information and crash videos can be combined to show that the occupant was "effectively restrained" between the roof and the seat. Analysis of the medical records of the other two occupants demonstrating that neither received any significant injury further debunks the defense argument that the occupant dove into the roof.

Consider another example: Assume for purposes of this illustration that a 21-year-old female is driving a late-model passenger automobile with her grandmother as a passenger in the automobile. She is struck from her left front by another vehicle that fails to yield the right-of-way at an intersection. She receives a closed head injury with a contusion to the left portion of her forehead and a horizontal laceration to her eyelid. The manufacturer argues that this occupant went to her left and struck the window sill, causing the horizontal laceration and head injury when her head hit either the window or the window sill and that the belt system could not provide effective restraint under these circumstance since the impact is more lateral than frontal. The plaintiff's argument is that the occupant went forward and to her left, striking the "A" pillar (windshield pillar) and that her injury was caused by the excessive slack in the shoulder portion of her belt, which is a design defect, combined with the belt not having locked until late in the accident sequence. The issue for the biomechanical witness revolves around the determination as to whether these injuries are tied to striking the "A" pillar or tied to striking the window and window sill. Valuation of the medical records demonstrates that the horizontal laceration to the eyebrow is an avulsion injury, which is a tearing of the skin. It is typically caused by the head sliding down some surface with friction from the impact causing a tearing of the skin. Thus, it can be demonstrated that this would not have occurred with a window nor would it have been caused by the window sill which is very broad, but rather it was caused by the narrow "A" pillar. Likewise, given the pattern of injury that would have occurred with a window strike or a strike to a broad surface as opposed to the contusion that was localized, indication striking a narrow surface, a biomechanical engineer can narrow down the objects that are available within the occupant compartment that would have caused this injury. In this example, the grandmother had classic bruises to the clavicle and a fractured sternum (indicating belt usage) while the plaintiff, despite eyewitness testimony about belt usage, had no bruising. Thus, the biomechanical expert can demonstrate by medical information and engineering analysis that the plaintiff's theory that the occupant was essentially unrestrained because of the slack in the belt system is accurate.

Determination of Occupant Kinematics

The biomechanical expert can often be very helpful in determining the occupant kinematics (movement of the occupant) in a given accident. Oftentimes the specific defect involved requires a determination as to whether the occupant was injured in the vehicle or outside of the vehicle. For example, take a case involving the allegation that a door latch is defective and that an occupant is thrown from a vehicle during an accident sequence due to the failure of the door to stay closed. The ultimate question as to injury causation becomes whether the occupant was injured while still in the vehicle or whether their injuries were caused by the ejection. In the example that I am using, the biomechanical engineer matched up scratches on the inside of the door frame with shoulder scratches on the deceased plaintiff to prove ejection through the door rather than through the window as alleged by the manufacturer. Other body contacts on the vehicle further confirmed the movement of the occupant. Finally, biomechanical expertise is particularly suited to a determination as to whether the trauma sustained is consistent with the contact with the ground or whether that contact would have had to come from some component part of the vehicle. The combination of human tolerance, specific injury causation evaluation, and physics of the movement of the occupant demonstrate in this case example an ejection that resulted in severe injury outside the vehicle.

Confirmation of Reconstruction

Typically, lawyers use mechanical engineers to reconstruct an accident and to explain the accident sequence to the jury. Consider the situation where a vehicle is maneuvered to avoid an animal; the driver, in response to his perception of the emergency, pulls on the parking brake and the vehicle begins to switch ends. During this maneuver, the vehicle is perpendicular to the road and, according to the plaintiff, rolls over. The defendants' reconstruction is that the driver turned the vehicle in the opposite direction from that alleged by the plaintiff's reconstructionist and that the rear of the vehicle slid off the roadway, causing the tires to contact the road surface (which is a couple of inches higher than the shoulder of the road) thus tripping the vehicle when it comes back onto the roadway. Hence, the jury is presented with totally opposite movements of the vehicle. The plaintiff's expert reconstructionist alleges a counterclockwise rotation of the vehicle and a passenger-side-leading roll; the defendants reconstructionist alleges a clockwise movement of the vehicle, a tripping of the vehicle by the roadway surface, and a driver-side-leading roll. How can the biomechanical engineer confirm your expert's reconstruction? In this case example, the biomechanical engineer analyzed the trajectory of the occupants and their individual injury patterns. The right-frontseat passenger, who was a small female, received a gouge to her skull from contact with the corner of the windshield frame on the passenger side. The expert was able to demonstrate that had this passenger been thrown towards the driver's side, she could not have physically come in contact with this portion of the vehicle. Likewise, the driver, who was thrown the furthest from the vehicle, would have ended up closest to the vehicle had the vehicle rolled in his direction rather than this individual being on the outside of the roll, traveling the greatest distance, and ending up a considerable distance from the vehicle. A similar analysis was done for the rear-seat passenger.

When the trajectory of all three occupants, tied to their individual injury patterns, was examined, it was clearly and easily demonstrated that the vehicle had to have rolled passenger-side first. This not only confirmed the plaintiff's accident reconstructionist but also addressed the alleged tripping of the vehicle in the defense reconstruction. Finally, as part of the process, it demonstrated that particularly gruesome nature of the cause of death. Consequently, in establishing causation, the biomechanical expert also tied all aspects of the case together and presented a nice package relating each area of expertise to the other areas.

§ 17.7 Conclusion

I have attempted to demonstrate that a biomechanical expert can be one of the most versatile and important weapons in the lawyer's arsenal, not only to analyze but also to prove liability and damages as part of proving causation. Biomechanics is a multifaceted discipline that combines aspects from engineering and medicine, thus providing the perfect transition between the liability and damages portion of the case. Fortunately, the expertise of this type of witness can also tie together the other aspects of the case, giving the jury a complete picture of the plaintiff's case.

TABLE OF CASES

Case	*Book §*
Breeden v. Valencial, Inc., 557 So. 2d 302 (La. Ct. App.) *writ denied*, 558 So. 2d 607 (La. 1990)	§ 17.5
Church v. Martin-Baker Aircraft Co., 643 F. Supp 499 (E.D. Mo. 1986)	§ 17.5
Mannino v. International Mfg. Co., 650 F.2d 846 (6th Cir. 1981)	§ 17.5

INDEX

BIOMECHANICAL ENGINEER
Qualifying § 17.5
Traditional legal rules § 17.5
BIOMECHANICAL EXPERT
Confirmation of reconstruction § 17.6
Occupant kinematics § 17.6
Seatbelt defense § 17.6
Tying injury to defect § 17.6
Use of §§ 17.4, 17.6
BIOMECHANICS OF INJURY
Generally §§ 17.1–17.7

DEFENSE'S ANNUITY EXPERT
Cross-examination § 15.7A

ENGINEERING PRINCIPLES
Application § 17.2

LIFE CARE PLAN
Home Modification § 9.11A

SPINAL CORD INJURY
Compression § 17.3
Distraction § 17.3
Extension § 17.3
Flexion § 17.3
Fractures, types of § 17.3
Mechanism of § 17.3
Miscellaneous § 17.3
SPINE
Anatomy of § 17.1

ISBN 0-7355-0072-X